Pets

PETS

A Warmhearted Look
At the Joys of Having a Pet

Edited by Beverly Simmons Bearly

Hallmark Editions

The publisher wishes to thank those who have given their kind permission to reprint material included in this book. Every effort has been made to give proper acknowledgments. Any omissions or errors are deeply regretted, and the publisher, upon notification, will be pleased to make necessary corrections in subsequent editions.

ACKNOWLEDGMENTS: "The Animal Store" from *Taxis and Toadstools* by Rachel Field. Copyright 1926 by Doubleday & Company, Inc. Reprinted by permission. "Pampered Pets" from *The Sound of Laughter* by Bennett Cerf. © 1970 by Bennett Cerf. Published by Doubleday & Company, Inc. Reprinted by permission. "pete at the seashore" from *Archy & Mehitabel* by Don Marquis. Copyright 1927. Published by Doubleday & Company, Inc. Reprinted by permission. "A Young Turkey" from *Pets at the White House* by Carl Carmer. Copyright © 1959, 1962 by Carl Carmer. Reprinted by permission of the publishers, E. P. Dutton & Co., Inc. "Bed-Time Story" by Melville H. Cane. Copyright, 1947, renewed, 1975, by Melville Cane. Reprinted from his volume, *And Pastures New,* by permission of Harcourt Brace Jovanovich, Inc. "Kola, the Bear" from pp. 10-11 in *Thanks to Noah* by George and Helen Waite Papashvily. Copyright, 1950, 1951 by George & Helen Waite Papashvily. Reprinted by permission of Harper & Row, Publishers, Inc. "What Is It?" from *A Pocketful of Poems* by Marie Louise Allen. Text copyright © 1957 by Marie Allen Howarth. Reprinted by permission of Harper & Row, Publishers, Inc. "Cat" from *Cats and People* by Frances and Richard Lockridge. Copyright 1950 by Frances and Richard Lockridge. Reprinted by permission of J. B. Lippincott Company, by the author and his agent, James Brown Associates, Inc. "The Porcupine" by Frances Frost from *The Little Naturalist.* Copyright 1929 by the Estate of Frances Frost & Kurt Werth. Published by Whittlesey House, a division of McGraw-Hill Book Company, Inc. Reprinted by permission. "Pony" by Betty Stoneham from "An Ode to the Shetland Pony" reprinted by permission of *Pony* Magazine. "Return to the Wild" from *Born Free,* by Joy Adamson. Copyright © 1960 by Joy Adamson. Reprinted by permission of Pantheon Books, a Division of Random House, Inc. and Wm. Collins Sons & Co. Ltd. "The History of the Dog" and "Cat History" © Pet Food Institute. Reprinted by permission. "I believe all kids should have pets...." from the book *Kids Say the Darndest Things* by Art Linkletter. © 1957 by Prentice-Hall, Inc. Published by Prentice-Hall, Inc., Englewood Cliffs, New Jersey. Reprinted by permission. "Harveya" by Henry Paul Jackson, "A Whooping Crane Pet" by S. W. Oliver and "Old Mame" by Miriam Pope Cimino from *Audubon Book of True Nature Stories,* selected and edited by John K. Terres. © 1958 by John K. Terres. Reprinted by permission.

Pets

What Is a Pet?

A pet is a playmate, a partner, a pleasure
Who brightens your life from the start —
A lovable, laughable, huggable treasure
Who wins a warm place in your heart.

A pet is a jester, a trickster, a teaser
Who's always prepared to perform —
A pouncer, a bouncer, a fetcher, a pleaser
Whose greeting is welcome and warm.

A pet is a blessing for so many reasons,
A gift of delight that endures —
A faithful companion, a friend for all seasons
Whose home, now and always, is yours!

Mary Catherine Shannon

A Young Turkey

Abraham Lincoln's son Tad had one of the more unusual pets to live at the White House. Here is an amusing story about Tad's turkey, Jack.

Election Day of 1864 was gloomy, and the dark clouds poured down a heavy rain on Washington. Since the soldiers stationed in Washington could not go home to vote, some of the states had sent commissions to Washington to set up voting facilities for these absentees. Pennsylvania had sent such a commission, and a regiment of "bucktails" as these men were called were voting on the lawn of the White House. Tad had seen them there and he ran into the office where Mr. Lincoln and Noah Brooks were sitting, begging his father to come to the window that he might see all the uniformed men "voting for Lincoln and Johnson." Looking out, the President saw not only the line of voters but Jack, the turkey, strutting among them in an interested way.

"What business has your turkey stalking about the voting polls in that way?" Mr. Lincoln asked his son. "Does he vote?"

"No," said Tad, "he is not of age."

Pampered Pets

Some people will do anything to please their pets. Here are a few examples.

1. The Earl of Cranbrook feeds his favorite bats on a choice mixture of egg yolk, cream cheese, and banana.
2. The number of new animal hospitals in the U.S. is going up nine times faster than new human hospitals.
3. The owner of a Great Dane dressed him up in top hat and tails so the dog wouldn't feel out of place at a fashionable wedding.
4. An Italian housewife was granted a divorce because her pet-loving spouse shared his bed with thirty cats and six dogs — and made her sleep in another room.
5. Two ladies in Louisville once inherited a $115,000 estate from a pampered goat named Sugar.
6. A New Yorker listed his dog's own personal phone number in the directory in case any of his friends felt the urge to call him.

> In today's world,
> only a dog can satisfy
> one's need to feel indispensable.
> *Ed Cunningham*

My Cat

My cat's a little mystery,
Part civilized, part wild —
As bold as jungle history,
As timid as a child,
As soft as any mitten,
As cunning as a thief,
A tiger playing kitten
In the shadow of a leaf,
A bit of this, a bit of that
And, oh, it's clear to see —
The more I get to know my cat,
The more I learn of me!

Sarah Norine Smith

The History of the Dog

Dogs or dog-like animals shared man's life 10,000 years ago. Archaeological records have established that by 3,500 B.C. distinctly different types of dogs were being kept as pets. In Egypt a greyhound-type dog was used for hunting; a dog similar to the Spitz lived in Europe. The Chinese owned tiny "sleeve dogs."

Domestication led to the development of different dogs for different tasks — dogs for warriors, hunters, scouts, retrievers, protectors, herders, messengers, dray animals and, of course, for pets.

There are more varieties or breeds of dogs than any other species of domestic animal. Dogs vary in size, coat, conformation and personality. The American Kennel Club recognizes 116 breeds with more added to the list from time to time.

Because the dog became an essential part of man's life, myths and legends about him came into being. The gods, too, owned dogs who were their friends, protectors and helpers, and they gave their dogs magical powers.

During the violence of the Middle Ages, packs of stray dogs, brought by conquering armies, terrorized the country folk so more legends sprang up, this time depicting supernatural dogs. Noblemen and land-owners kept dogs for hunting and housepets. Peasants bred dogs to guard their flocks, pull carts, and hunt small game such as rabbits, rats and badgers. Whether he was owned by a lord or a peasant, the dog was admired for his intelligence, courage, faithfulness and affectionate nature. Then, as now, he was called man's best friend.

I Am a Cat

I enjoy being a cat, and I never try to act like anything else. If I don't seem bright eyed and bushy tailed all day long, please don't think I'm aloof or smugly independent or ungrateful for your hospitality. It's just that I'm a deep thinker, and sometimes I need a little privacy. When we get to know each other better, you'll find me playful, affectionate, loyal and very good company. In fact, I think you'll agree that there is no finer pet in all the world. Forgive me if I sound vain, but it is in my nature to be honest and proud. I am a cat.

Ed Cunningham

Animals are such agreeable friends — they ask no questions, they pass no criticisms. *George Eliot*

God gave man the cat in order that he might have the pleasure of caressing the tiger. *Proverb*

11

Pony

You stood upon the springy turf
So small and yet so strong,
You gazed at me with gentle eyes,
And as you idly swished those flies
That flew in never ending streams —
I saw the idol of my dreams.

Betty Stoneham

Kola, the Bear

Having raised Kola the bear almost from birth, George Papashvily regarded him as more of a pal than a pet. Here he describes his attempts to curb Kola's curiosity and to teach him manners.

Once workmen came from the city to build a fine house for a prince. After a few days passed I had a complaint from the carpenter that Kola had growled at him.

From then on I kept Kola at home during the day. But nights he went back there and climbed all over the scaffold — not to hurt anything, but just so he would know, too, the same as the rest of us, how a prince's house gets built.

The carpenter found out and so on purpose he left a cross plank with the far end resting on air. When Kola stepped there it threw him to the ground and bruised him so bad he couldn't walk for a week.

After that Kola waited his chance until one night the carpenter forgot to put all of his tools away. The next day the hammer was gone. While the carpenter searched everywhere Kola sat on it and watched, picking his teeth with his long claws and laughing from the side of his muzzle as only bears can.

Naturally I scolded Kola for disgracing us with such actions. But when the whole story came out and the stonecutters on the job told Kola's side, the carpenter was most to blame. He started it by giving Kola the first time he saw him tobacco soaked in honey to tease him.

The best I could I tried to show Kola not to be mean and pay back bad with worse. Only it was hard when human beings set him such kind of an example.

The Horse

I will not change my horse with any that treads...
When I bestride him, I soar, I am a hawk.
He trots the air; the earth sings when he touches it.
The basest horn of his hoof is more musical than the
    pipe of Hermes...
He's of the color of the nutmeg and of the heat of
    the ginger...
He is pure air and fire, and the dull elements
Of earth and water never appear in him,
But only in patient stillness while his rider mounts him...
It is the prince of palfreys. His neigh is like
The bidding of a monarch, and his countenance
Enforces homage.   *William Shakespeare*

pete at the seashore

i ran along the yellow sand
and made the sea gulls fly
i chased them down the waters edge
i chased them up the sky

i ran so hard i ran so fast
i left the spray behind
i chased the flying flecks of foam
and i outran the wind

an airplane sailing overhead
climbed when it heard me bark
i yelped and leapt right at the sun
until the sky grew dark

some little children on the beach
threw sticks and ran with me
o master let us go again
and play beside the sea
                    pete the pup
                        Don Marquis

Cat History

The house cat's origins are shrouded in mystery. He strolled into recorded history looking very much like he does today.

The cats of ancient Egypt, portrayed in sacred statues and hieroglyphics, resemble short-haired cats of today. Pictures of fluffy ancestors of today's Persians adorn very old oriental scrolls. Sanskrit writing dating back to 3,000 B.C. mentions the cat.

Probably the cat was domesticated for two reasons — to catch mice and to provide amusement. The Egyptians used the cat to protect their rich stores of grain. By 2,000 B.C., a religious cult centered around the cat. Chief diety was a cat-headed goddess, Pasht or Bastet. From her name the word "puss" is derived.

When the family cat died, it was laid to rest with elaborate ceremony. Egyptian cat mummies can be seen in museums.

Exporting cats was prohibited by Egyptian law, but the wily Phoenician traders smuggled them to other Mediterranean countries. Later, the Romans took pet cats to Ireland, Great Britain, France and other parts of the empire.

Cats, as symbols to be venerated, appear in the temple decorations and religious ceremonies of India, the Far East, and Near Eastern countries.

Because of pagan cat worship, medieval Christians

thought the cat was a consort of witches and Satan. (Puss's quiet, mysterious ways did nothing to dispel this idea.) Cats were cruelly persecuted in medieval times. The cat's skill as a rodent killer may have saved him from extinction in Europe.

The plagues came, carried by rats, so once again he was needed for protection, and once again his charm made him a treasured household pet.

Settlers coming to the New World brought cats to grace the hearth and protect the granary. Puss traveled in covered wagons and sailing ships the length and breadth of the Americas.

The Porcupine

This spiky fellow, black and white,
Sleeps all day and plays all night.
He waddles from his hollow tree
Across the evening yard to see
If I've put out his bacon dish.
He never gives his tail a swish
But keeps his barbs flat; still I wish
His middle ribs were not so tickly.
I'd pat him if he weren't so prickly!

Frances Frost

What Is It?

Tall ears,
Twinkly nose,
Tiny tail,
And — hop he goes!

What is he —
Can you guess?
I feed him carrots
And watercress.

His ears are long,
His tail is small —
And he doesn't make any
Noise at all!

Tall ears,
Twinkly nose,
Tiny tail,
And — hop, he goes!

Marie Louise Allen

A Duck Named Josh

I once had the most well behaved, well trained duck in the county. Josh never quacked at night, always shook his head "Thank you" when he was fed and, above all, never tracked water through the house. To tell the truth, sometimes Josh seemed — well — almost too perfect; that is, until the Christmas we discovered that popcorn isn't only for people.

Now popcorn is a snack that was rarely visible around our home because it was devoured practically before it finished popping! But every Christmas we'd decorate our tree with long, lush popcorn strings and have to be satisfied with just looking.

Just before the holidays the first year I had Josh, the weather turned very cold. I carried Josh into the house to keep him warm; but instead of lying calmly and snugly on the living room rug as usual, he dove right underneath the Christmas tree. In fact, my quiet, staid duck kept pecking at the lower branches. Finally I pulled him away and fed him a crust of bread to keep him busy while I was in the kitchen. Suddenly I heard a crash and what sounded like an entire flock of ducks! There was Josh, peeking out from under the fallen tree, quacking his head off and gobbling up every kernel of popcorn in sight — string and all!

The tree wasn't hurt much and, luckily, neither was Josh. But we kept him in the barn around Christmas after that. He didn't mind though. Each year he'd get the gift he liked best of all — a big bowl of popcorn for his very own.   *Blanche Weiss*

Cat

She sits on the floor, front paws together in unexampled neatness, tail curved to body....Her eyes are...completely round and formed of concentric circles with the pupil, which can become a slit when she chooses, a black depth not to be fathomed. Otherwise her eyes are blue. She appears expectant, but it is impossible to guess what she expects.

Richard Lockridge

I believe all kids should have pets. It's an essential part of growing up. There's a mystic kinship between a boy and his dog, a sharing of love and trust that's unique. A boy's dog is his pal, his companion, his comforter when tears come, and his best listener to whispered secrets. At the price of a dog tag and a bowl of food each day, a pup's probably the biggest bargain in any kid's life.   *Art Linkletter*

Pets

Pets are truly
Courteous folk:
They do not drink,
They do not smoke,
They do not cuss
Or gripe or grouse
Or tell you how
To run your house.
They never nag
Or give offense.
Pets are perfect
Ladies and Gents!

Shifra Stein

A Whooping Crane Pet

S.W. Oliver writes of finding a wounded whooping crane and bringing him home.

We decided to let the bird make his own choice as to whether or not he wished to take his freedom or stay with us. One morning we brought him out in the yard and let him go. Stretching himself and shaking his wings he walked about looking things over, then began picking up bits to eat, as much as to say, "This suits me fine, I will stay." And stay he did for about three years....

We named him "Bill" after a neighbor boy of about the same gangly build. In a short while he learned to recognize his name and would come when called, even if he was out of sight. I would let him get a quarter of a mile on his way up the creek bottom to feed and would then call "Bill!" He would stop, answer me, and come back....

One night in June Bill did not come home. We did not worry for he had stayed away overnight before. After several days, and still he had not come home, we began to worry for fear that something might have happened to him. We searched all the ponds and sloughs for miles around but could not find him. One morning after he had been gone for two weeks, I heard a faint trumpet call way off to the southwest. I strained my ears to get the next call and sure enough it was

26

nearer, and soon I saw a speck away off in the distance. It was Bill, flying higher than usual, showing he had come from a great distance. When within a half mile of the house he began to drop down and how he whooped, one whoop after another, as fast as he could, seeming to want to let us know that he was coming and his joy at being home again. Soon he swooped into the yard a little below where we were all standing and came up to us as fast as he could walk, talking loud and fast and showing his pleasure at seeing all of us again.

Winston Churchill was strongly attached to his French poodle, Rufus, and tried to spare it any distress.

At Chequers, whenever he watched a movie, he would hold the poodle on his lap. If a situation developed on the screen which might conceivably be disturbing to Rufus, Churchill would cover the dog's eyes with his hand and keep it there until the scene was over.

> **B**y associating with the cat,
> one only risks becoming richer.
> *Colette*

What Is a Puppy?

A puppy's a lively affectionate creature,
A magical, marvelous toy,
A comic, a cutup, a lighthearted teacher
Whose lessons are laughter and joy.

A puppy's a mischievous madcap by day,
A vigilant watchdog by night,
A pleasure when everything's going your way,
A comfort when nothing goes right.

A puppy's a pet who just loves being petted,
A friend who is steadfast and true,
A helper to whom you are ever indebted —
A puppy's a pet who owns you!

Mary Ann Coyle

Harveya

Harveya, a black-tailed jackrabbit, became the pet of Henry Paul Jackson when she was a baby. Here he describes Harveya's reaction to a spanking.

When she was small I would let her outside on her own, and she would return through the open door in about an hour. But one day I paddled her lightly with a piece of paper for some indiscretion, perhaps for jumping onto the dining table or an open bed. Intelligent as she was, she soon learned by this method of punishment what she shouldn't do. The next day, when I let her out to run a little, she stayed out for forty hours! It was a moonlit night, and far and wide I roamed, searching for her; but I did not find Harveya.

That evening, as I sat at the dinner table with guests, I heard Harveya scratch at the sliding door to the patio. I opened the door and Harveya came up to me. I was overjoyed at her return. She lay down at my feet for me to pick her up, which I did with pleasure! Soon she went to the refrigerator and assumed her asking position. I got up from the table to get her some milk; and she followed me, standing up on her hind legs, to the amusement of my guests. I am sure that she was as glad to be home as I was to have her. I might add that every one of us enjoyed our dinner after that. I know that my appetite was restored.

The Family Circle

How does she manage such symmetry?
She curls in a circle so perfectly —
A symbol of love, this ring of fur,
To show us our family revolves around her!

Gail Peterson

My Lamb

There's nothing, no nothing,
as soft as my lamb,
nothing else in the world.
Not clouds or even butterfly wings.
Nothing as soft as my lamb.
There's no pet as sweet
as my lamb — anywhere.
He's my dearest friend.
When he presses
his cold little nose in my hand
and gives me a kiss with his tongue,
I know he's the very best pet
in the world.
I love him,
my own little lamb.

Rebecca Peterson

Pet Peeves

Thou shalt not bringeth me to shame
By calling me a cute-sy name.
Thou shalt not putteth me through my paces
In front of unfamiliar faces.
Thou shalt not causeth me to squawk
Or beggeth for my daily walk.
Thou shalt not curse and climbeth the walls
When I respondeth to nature's calls.
Thou shalt not shruggeth off my ills
But forketh over for shots and pills.
Thou shalt not let *thy* diet dictate
How much goes on *my* dinner plate.
Thou shalt not forgetteth all year through —
My happiness dependeth on you!

Elizabeth Plowman

Return to the Wild

To Elsa, a young lioness, George and Joy Adamson were the only parents she'd ever known. The three constituted a very happy family until the Adamsons began the difficult (and successful) attempt of returning Elsa to the world of the wild. Mrs. Adamson tells of a reunion after they had left Elsa on her own for a few days.

When we arrived at our former camp we looked at once for her pugmarks; there was no sign of them. I began to call. Soon afterward we heard her familiar "hnk-hnk" and saw her coming from the river trotting as fast as she could. Her welcome showed us that she had missed us as much as we had missed her and her rubbings and miaowings touched us deeply. We had brought her a buck, but she hardly glanced at it and continued her greetings. As soon as the great rejoicings were over I looked at her stomach: it was full. She must have eaten recently; this took a great load off my mind for it meant that she was now safe. She had proved that she could fend for herself and be independent of us, at least so far as food was concerned.

While our tents were being pitched I took her to the river and there we rested together. I was happy now and could relax, feeling that Elsa's future was assured. She must have felt the same, for she laid her big soft paw on me and dozed off.

The Animal Store

If I had a hundred dollars to spend,
　　Or maybe a little more,
I'd hurry as fast as my legs would go
　　Straight to the animal store.

I wouldn't say, "How much for this or that?"
　　"What kind of dog is he?"
I'd buy as many as rolled an eye,
　　Or wagged a tail at me!

I'd take the hound with the drooping ears
　　That sits by himself alone;
Cockers and Cairns and wobbly pups
　　For to be my very own.

I might buy a parrot all red and green,
　　And the monkey I saw before,
If I had a hundred dollars to spend,
　　Or maybe a little more.

Rachel Field

Cats are a mysterious kind of folk.
There is more passing in their
minds than we are aware of.

Sir Walter Scott

Old Mame

A large gray squirrel became "Old Mame," friend and pet of Miriam Pope Cimino. Here she describes Old Mame's party manners.

Let us get a gathering in the back garden and there, always, was Old Mame. Watching at a discreet distance as guests arrived, she stood upright, with her paws neatly folded over her white apron, like a little old neighbor woman getting an eyeful. There is not a canape tidbit she refused, even if she had to bury it in disgust the next moment. And regardless of the number of people at our garden party she selected my husband as the giver. He was the one who allowed her to run up his legs and sit begging for something to eat.

One more thing we learned — that it *is* possible for a wild creature to *like* being near you without benefit of handouts. There were times when, completely sated, and tired of burying things, she was content to sit quietly near us where we were seated on our garden chairs.

The dog was created specially for children.
He is the god of frolic.

Henry Ward Beecher

My Fish

My fish
Swish,
Blowing bubbles,
Iridescent
Blue and green,
Swimming
In between
Each other,
Diving,
Surfacing once more,
Skimming over
The glass-bottomed floor,
Cutting the water
Like a knife,
Carefree,
Bubbling
With life —
My fish
Swish.

Katherine Nelson Davis

Favorite Sound

Some prefer "meow,"
Others, "bow-wow,"
But my home's complete
With a sweet "tweet-tweet!"
Gail Peterson

Bed-Time Story

Melville Cane in Bed-Time Story *compares his animals who unite for common cause, with the United Nations. In the last two lines an important question is asked which "daddy" neatly sidetracks. Perhaps the future will provide the right and happy answer.*

Once there was a spaniel
By the name of Daniel,
And a pig,
Sig,
And a pussy,
Gussie —
She chased a mouse,
Klaus;
And a squirrel,
Errol,
And a white she-bear,
Claire,
And a Scotch lion,
Ian,
And a very fierce shark,
Mark.

You'll agree, my dear,
They were rather a queer
Assortment
Of temperament and deportment.

And yet,
My pet,
In spite of their diversities
And perversities
Both zoological
And ideological,
They all gathered together
One day, when the weather
Was especially frightful, and decided
It wasn't safe to stay divided
Any longer, and that they should,
For their common good,
(Rather than risk another calamity)
Try amity.

And that's the way there began to dawn a
Plan they christened United Fauna.

"And did they live happily ever after, daddy?"
"I'll tell you the rest tomorrow. Good-night, dear."

The Truest Friend

A dog is a comfort,
  an ally in a sometimes unfriendly world.
A dog is a welcoming committee
  that lets you know you're home, all right!
A dog is the certainty that home is where you most
  want to be.
A dog is a chance to express yourself
  without the fear of seeming foolish,
a chance to share emotions that others of our kind
  too often repel — tenderness, outright joy, love.
A dog hears your secret needs and sympathizes
  or artfully distracts you from your woes.
A dog defeats loneliness, defies unhappiness
  and teaches hard humans the virtue of play.
A dog gives you the feeling, however untrue,
  that you're worth his affection.
A dog holds to values this world has forgotten —
  duty, loyalty, respect.
A dog will obey you, bestowing upon a master
  power one's own children come to challenge.
Most of all, especially in times like these,
  a dog is the truest and most reliable friend.

Gail Peterson

45

PHOTOGRAPHERS:
Phoebe Dunn: *page 21;* Dale Durfee: *pages 4, 41;*
Richard Fanolio: *pages 9, 28, 44;*
Harv Gariety: *dust jacket, page 13;*
Carol Hale: *pages 25, 33;* Maxine Jacobs: *page 36;*
Roger Marshutz: *page 16;* Nancy Mathews: *title page.*

Text and titles set in ITC Souvenir, an informal,
contemporary typeface designed by Edward Benguiat.
Printed on Hallmark Crown Royale Book paper.
Designed by Bruce Baker.